Children's Verse

The Batsford Book of

CHILDREN'S VERSE

EDITED BY ELIZABETH JENNINGS

B. T. BATSFORD LTD. LONDON

For
Mark, Gillian and Judith

FIRST PUBLISHED, 1958

PRINTED AND BOUND IN THE NETHERLANDS
BY L. VAN LEER AND CO. LTD., LONDON AND AMSTERDAM
FOR THE PUBLISHERS
B. T. BATSFORD LTD.
4, FITZHARDINGE STREET, PORTMAN SQUARE, LONDON, W.1

Preface

IN putting together this book of verse, I have tried to bear in mind two things especially. The first is that one can never be absolutely sure what a child will or will not like in the way of poetry; for this reason, I have done my best to recall, as truthfully as possible, my own literary taste in childhood. And secondly, I feel very strongly that children often greatly enjoy what they do not totally understand: they are at home among mysteries. The explanation for this is obvious; the imagination of a child is unspoilt by habit or preconceived notions. He can therefore *give* to a verse or a rhyme as much, almost, as he takes from it. This does not mean that he is satisfied with the second-rate or the incomplete; on the contrary, the child is quick to detect the bogus because his own faculties have not been impaired by misuse or custom.

Many of the poems in this collection are famous, and rightly famous. Any anthology which set out to include only what was little-known would be idiosyncratic to the point of ludicrousness. I have, however, gathered together a number of poems, by living and dead poets, which might not, at first glance, seem especially suitable for children. My touchstone in the selection of such pieces has been my own predilections in childhood and also the belief that nothing which is direct, fresh and honest is alien to a child's mind.

Many moods are reflected here, and many themes represented. I have made room for poems of action and of the heroic temper and, on the other hand, for poems of observation and reflection. I am not very much in favour of anthologies which divide poems rigidly into groups because this kind of arrangement tends both to separate poems arbitrarily and also, paradoxically, to join together poems which have nothing in common, perhaps, save their subject-matter. Nevertheless, these poems *do* fall into a plan, a plan which, I hope, will become more and more evident as the book is travelled through. But the book does not *have* to be read in this way, of course. Nor, indeed, is it probable that any one reader will like *all* the poems which are printed here.

I should like now to add a little to what I have already said about children loving mysterious things. Doubtless, there are words, phrases, lines, in some of these poems which will not immediately yield their meanings to a child. Yet children have a strange knack of following passages which might appear obscure to an older reader; I think this is because they seldom come to poems with prejudices or preconceptions. This, at least, has been my own experience when I have read poems to school-children. Where I have selected the work of living writers, I have chosen poems which appear to me to be both lucid and also packed with hints and suggestions. One thing I am quite certain of is that children are almost always suspicious of, even antagonistic to, poems written especially for them. It is so perilously difficult not to write down to children and condescension is one of the things they are most keenly aware of.

Most of these poems read well aloud and I think that music, cadence, emphasis are essential in a book of verse such as this. Nowhere, however, have I selected poems purely for their *sound*. Even the nonsense rhymes printed here have a very definite meaning and purpose.

The illustrations accompanying these poems should not be regarded simply as comments on the texts, and certainly not as elucidations of the poems. The poems and the pictures complement one another and all are intended to give *pleasure*. If the poems also help to develop a taste for poetry in one or two readers, then this book will have achieved even more than its main purpose.

ELIZABETH JENNINGS

Contents

Acknowledgment

The Author and Publishers would like to thank the following for permission to include certain copyright poems:

W. H. Auden, "Miranda's Song" (from *For the Time Being*): Messrs Faber & Faber Ltd

Hilaire Belloc, "George" (from *Cautionary Tales*): Messrs Gerald Duckworth & Co. Ltd; "The End of the Road" (from *The Path to Rome*): Messrs George Allen & Unwin Ltd

Roy Campbell, (from *Choosing a Mast*): the executrix Mrs Roy Campbell; John Lane, The Bodley Head

G. K. Chesterton, "Lepanto" (from *Collected Poems of G. K. Chesterton*): Miss D. E. Collins; "The Donkey" (from *The Wild Knight and Other Poems*): Miss D. E. Collins; Messrs J. M. Dent & Sons Ltd

W. H. Davies, "Street Criers" (from *The Collected Poems of W. H. Davies*): Mrs H. M. Davies; Messrs Jonathan Cape Ltd

Walter de la Mare, "The Bees' Song" and "The Song of the Shadows" (from *Peacock Pie*): The Literary Trustees of Walter de la Mare; Messrs Faber & Faber Ltd

Lawrence Durrell, "Echo" (from *Selected Poems of Lawrence Durrell*): Messrs Faber & Faber Ltd

T. S. Eliot, "Gus: the Theatre Cat" (from *Old Possum's Book of Practical Cats*): Messrs Faber & Faber Ltd

Christopher Fry (from *The Lady's not for Burning*): Oxford University Press

Robert Graves, "Warning to children" (from *Collected Poems*) (1914-1947): Messrs Cassell & Co. Ltd

Thomas Hardy, "Weathers" (from *Collected Poems of Thomas Hardy*): The Trustees of the Hardy Estate; Messrs Macmillan & Co. Ltd

Gerard Manley Hopkins, from "The Blessed Virgin Compared to the Air we Breathe" (from *Poems of Gerard Manley Hopkins*): Oxford University Press

Sidney Keys, "The Gardener" (from *Collected Poems of Sidney Keys*): Messrs Routledge & Kegan Paul Ltd

Rudyard Kipling, "Runnymede" (from *The Definitive Edition of Rudyard Kipling's Verse*): Mrs George Bembridge

Philip Larkin, "At Grass" (from *The Less Deceived*): The Marvell Press

Laurie Lee, "Field of Autumn" (from *The Bloom of Candles*): Laurie Lee

C. Day Lewis, from "O dreams, O destinations" (from *Word Over All*): Messrs Jonathan Cape Ltd

Edwin Muir, "The Bird" (from *Collected Poems of Edwin Muir*): Messrs Faber & Faber Ltd

F. T. Prince, "The Token" (from *Poems of F. T. Prince*): Messrs Faber & Faber Ltd

Kathleen Raine, "In the Beck" (from *Collected Poems of Kathleen Raine*): Messrs Hamish Hamilton Ltd

John Crowe Ransom, "Blue Girls" (from *Selected Poems of John Crowe Ransom*): Pearn, Pollinger & Higham Ltd; Alfred A. Knopf Inc., New York

Ann Ridler, "Now Philippa is gone" (from *The Nine Bright Shiners*): Messrs Faber & Faber Ltd

Theodore Roethke, "The Lady and the Bear" (from *Words for the Wind*): Messrs Secker & Warburg

Stevie Smith, "My Cats" (from *Harold's Leap*): Messrs Chapman & Hall Ltd

Stephen Spender, "My parents kept me from children who were rough" (from *Collected Poems of Stephen Spender*): Messrs Faber & Faber Ltd

Edward Thomas, "Out in the Dark": Mrs Helen Thomas

W. B. Yeats "The Peacock" and "The Wild Swans at Coole" (from *Collected Poems by W. B. Yeats*): Mrs Yeats; Messrs Macmillan & Co. Ltd

The Illustrations

Answer to a Child's Question

Do you ask what the birds say? The sparrow, the dove,
The linnet and thrush say, 'I love and I love!'
In the winter they're silent, the wind is so strong;
What it says I don't know, but it sings a loud song.
But green leaves, and blossoms, and sunny warm weather,
And singing and loving—all come back together.
But the lark is so brimful of gladness and love,
The green fields below him, the blue sky above,
That he sings, and he sings, and for ever sings he,
'I love my Love, and my Love loves me.'

SAMUEL TAYLOR COLERIDGE

"My parents kept me from children who were rough"

My parents kept me from children who were rough
And who threw words like stones and who wore torn clothes.
Their thighs showed through rags. They ran in the street
And climbed cliffs and stripped by the country streams.

I feared more than tigers their muscles like iron
And their jerking hands and their knees tight on my arms.
I feared the salt coarse pointing of those boys
Who copied my lisp behind me on the road.

They were lithe, they sprang out behind hedges
Like dogs to bark at our world. They threw mud
And I looked another way, pretending to smile.
I longed to forgive them, yet they never smiled.

STEPHEN SPENDER

My True-Love

My true-love hath my heart and I have his,
By just exchange one to the other given:
I hold his dear, and mine he cannot miss,
There never was a better bargain driven:
    My true-love hath my heart and I have his.

His heart in me keeps him and me in one,
My heart in him his thoughts and senses guides:
He loves my heart, for once it was his own,
I cherish his because in me it bides:
    My true-love hath my heart and I have his.

SIR PHILIP SIDNEY

The Woodspurge

THE wind flapped loose, the wind was still,
Shaken out dead from tree and hill:
I had walked out at the wind's will,—
I sat now, for the wind was still.

Between my knees my forehead was,—
My lips, drawn in, said not Alas!
My hair was over in the grass,
My naked ears heard the day pass.

My eyes, wide open, had the run
Of some ten weeds to fix upon;
Among those few, out of the sun,
The woodspurge flowered, three cups in one.

From perfect grief there need not be
Wisdom or even memory:
One thing then learnt remains to me,—
The woodspurge has a cup of three.

DANTE GABRIEL ROSSETTI

Blue Girls

Twirling your blue skirts, travelling the sward
Under the towers of your seminary,
Go listen to your teachers old and contrary
Without believing a word.

Tie the white fillets then about your hair
And think no more of what will come to pass
Than blue birds that go walking on the grass
And chattering on the air.

Practise your beauty, blue girls, before it fail;
And I will cry with my loud lips and publish
Beauty which all our power shall never establish,
It is so frail.

For I could tell you a story which is true;
I know a lady with a terrible tongue,
Blear eyes fallen from blue,
All her perfections tarnished—yet it is not long
Since she was lovelier than any of you.

JOHN CROWE RANSOM

Warning to children

CHILDREN, if you dare to think
Of the greatness, rareness, muchness,
Fewness of this precious only
Endless world in which you say
You live, you think of things like this:
Blocks of slate enclosing dappled
Red and green, enclosing tawny
Yellow nets, enclosing white
And black acres of dominoes,
Where a neat brown paper parcel
Tempts you to untie the string.
In the parcel a small island,
On the island a large tree,
On the tree a husky fruit.
Strip the husk and pare the rind off:
In the kernel you will see
Blocks of slate enclosed by dappled
Red and green, enclosed by tawny
Yellow nets, enclosed by white
And black acres of dominoes,
Where the same brown paper parcel—
Children, leave the string untied!
For who dares undo the parcel
Finds himself at once inside it,
On the island, in the fruit,
Blocks of slate about his head,
Finds himself enclosed by dappled
Green and red, enclosed by yellow

Tawny nets, enclosed by black
And white acres of dominoes,
With the same brown paper parcel
Still untied upon his knee.
And, if he then should dare to think
Of the fewness, muchness, rareness,
Greatness of this endless only
Precious world in which he says
He lives—he then unties the string.

ROBERT GRAVES

Spring and Fall: to a young child

MARGARET, are you grieving
Over Goldengrove unleaving?
Leaves, like the things of man, you
With your fresh thoughts care for, can you?
Ah! as the heart grows older
It will come to such sights colder
By and by, nor spare a sigh
Though worlds of wanwood leafmeal lie;
And yet you will weep and know why.
Now no matter, child, the name:
Sorrow's springs are the same.
Nor mouth had, no nor mind, expressed
What heart heard of, ghost guessed:
It is the blight man was born for,
It is Margaret you mourn for.

GERARD MANLEY HOPKINS

The Handsome Heart:
at a gracious answer

But tell me, child, your choice; what shall I buy
You?'—'Father, what you buy me I like best.'
With the sweetest air that said, still plied and pressed,
He swung to his first poised purport of reply.

What the heart is! which, like carriers let fly—
Doff darkness, homing nature knows the rest—
To its own fine function, wild and self-instressed,
Falls light as ten years long taught how to and why.

Mannerly-hearted! more than handsome face—
Beauty's bearing or muse of mounting vein,
All, in this case, bathed in high hallowing grace . . .

Of heaven what boon to buy you, boy, or gain
Not granted!—Only . . . O on that path you pace
Run all your race, O brace sterner than strain!

GERARD MANLEY HOPKINS

The Token

MORE beautiful than any gift you gave
You were, a child so beautiful as to seem
To promise ruin what no child can have
Or woman give. And so a Roman gem
I choose to be your token: here a laurel
Springs to its young height, hangs a broken limb.
And here a group of women wanly quarrel
At a sale of Cupids. A hawk looks at them.

F. T. PRINCE

From-'Ode on Intimations of Immortality'

There was a time when meadow, grove, and stream,
The earth, and every common sight,
    To me did seem
    Apparelled in celestial light,
The glory and the freshness of a dream.
It is not now as it hath been of yore;—
    Turn wheresoe'er I may,
      By night or day,
The things which I have seen I now can see no more.

    The Rainbow comes and goes,
    And lovely is the Rose,
    The Moon doth with delight
Look round her when the heavens are bare,
    Waters on a starry night
    Are beautiful and fair;
The sunshine is a glorious birth;
But yet I know, where'er I go,
That there hath pass'd away a glory from the earth.

Our birth is but a sleep and a forgetting:
The Soul that rises with us, our life's Star,
    Hath had elsewhere its setting,
    And cometh from afar:
    Not in entire forgetfulness,
    And not in utter nakedness,
But trailing clouds of glory do we come
    From God, who is our home:
Heaven lies about us in our infancy!

Shades of the prison-house begin to close
   Upon the growing Boy,
But He beholds the light, and whence it flows,
   He sees it in his joy;
The Youth who daily farther from the east
    Must travel, still is Nature's Priest,
    And by the vision splendid
    Is on his way attended;
At length the Man perceives it die away,
And fade into the light of common day.

WILLIAM WORDSWORTH

From-'O dreams, O destinations'

CHILDREN look down upon the morning-grey
Tissue of mist that veils a valley's lap:
Their fingers itch to tear it and unwrap
The flags, the roundabouts, the gala day.
They watch the spring rise inexhaustibly—
A breathing thread out of the eddied sand,
Sufficient to their day: but half their mind
Is on the sailed and glittering estuary.
Fondly we wish their mist might never break,
Knowing it hides so much that best were hidden:
We'd chain them by the spring, lest it should broaden
For them into a quicksand or a wreck.
But they slip through our fingers like the source,
Like mist, like time that has flagged out their course.

CECIL DAY LEWIS

From-'The Prelude'

ONE evening (surely I was led by her)
I went alone into a Shepherd's Boat,
A Skiff that to a Willow tree was tied
Within a rocky Cave, its usual home.
'Twas by the shores of Patterdale, a Vale
Wherein I was a Stranger, thither come
A School-boy Traveller, at the Holidays.
Forth rambled from the Village Inn alone
No sooner had I sight of this small Skiff,
Discover'd thus by unexpected chance,
Than I unloos'd her tether and embark'd.
The moon was up, the Lake was shining clear
Among the hoary mountains; from the Shore
I push'd, and struck the oars and struck again
In cadence, and my little Boat mov'd on
Even like a Man who walks with stately step
Though bent on speed. It was an act of stealth
And troubled pleasure; not without the voice
Of mountain-echoes did my Boat move on,
Leaving behind her still on either side
Small circles glittering idly in the moon,
Until they melted all into one track
Of sparkling light. A rocky Steep uprose
Above the Cavern of the Willow tree
And now, as suited one who proudly row'd
With his best skill, I fix'd a steady view
Upon the top of that same craggy ridge,
The bound of the horizon, for behind
Was nothing but the stars and the grey sky.

She was an elfin Pinnace; lustily
I dipp'd my oars into the silent Lake,
And, as I rose upon the stroke, my Boat
Went heaving through the water, like a Swan;
When from behind that craggy Steep, till then
The bound of the horizon, a huge Cliff,
As if with voluntary power instinct,
Uprear'd its head.   I struck, and struck again,
And, growing still in stature, the huge Cliff
Rose up between me and the stars, and still,
With measur'd motion, like a living thing,
Strode after me. With trembling hands I turn'd,
And through the silent water stole my way
Back to the Cavern of the Willow tree.

WILLIAM WORDSWORTH

Upon a child that died

Here she lies, a pretty bud,
Lately made of flesh and blood:
Who as soon fell fast asleep
As her little eyes did peep.
Give her strewings, but not stir
The earth that lightly covers her.

ROBERT HERRICK

From- 'Lepanto'

Wʜɪᴛᴇ founts falling in the courts of the sun,
And the Soldan of Byzantium is smiling as they run;
There is laughter like the fountains in that face of all men feared,
It stirs the forest darkness, the darkness of his beard,
It curls the blood-red crescent, the crescent of his lips,
For the inmost sea of all the world is shaken with his ships.
They have dared the white republics up the capes of Italy,
They have dashed the Adriatic round the Lion of the Sea
And the Pope has cast his arms abroad for agony and loss,
And called the kings of Christendom for swords about the Cross,
The cold queen of England is looking in the glass;
The shadow of the Valois is yawning at the Mass;
From evening isles fantastical rings faint the Spanish gun,
And the Lord upon the golden Horn is laughing in the sun.

Dim drums throbbing, in the hills half heard,
Where only on a nameless throne a crownless prince has stirred,
Where, risen from a doubtful seat and half-attainted stall,
The last knight of Europe takes weapons from the wall,
The last and lingering troubadour to whom the bird has sung,
That once went singing southward when all the world was young,
In that enormous silence, tiny and unafraid,
Comes up along a winding road the noise of the Crusade.
Strong gongs groaning as the guns boom far,
Don John of Austria is going to the war,
Stiff blasts straining in the night-blasts cold
In the gloom black-purple, in the glint old-gold,
Torchlight crimson on the copper kettle-drums,
Then the tuckets, then the trumpets, then the cannon,
    and he comes.

Don John laughing in the brave beard curled,
Spurning of his stirrups like the thrones of all the world,
Holding his head up for a flag of all the free.
Love-light of Spain—hurrah!
Death-light of Africa!
Don John of Austria
Is riding to the sea.

G. K. CHESTERTON

Meeting at night

THE grey sea and the long black land;
And the yellow half-moon large and low;
And the startled little waves that leap
In fiery ringlets from their sleep,
As I gain the cove with pushing prow,
And quench its speed i' the slushy sand.

Then a mile of warm sea-scented beach;
Three fields to cross till a farm appears;
A tap at the pane, the quick sharp scratch
And blue spurt of a lighted match,
And a voice less loud, thro' its joys and fears
Than the two hearts beating each to each!

ROBERT BROWNING

From-'Christabel'

A LITTLE child, a limber elf,
Singing, dancing to itself,
A fairy thing with red round cheeks,
That always finds, and never seeks,
Makes such a vision to the sight
As fills a father's eyes with light;
And pleasures flow in so thick and fast
Upon his heart, that he at last
Must needs express his love's excess
With words of unmeant bitterness.
Perhaps 'tis pretty to force together
Thoughts so all unlike each other;
To mutter and mock a broken charm,
To dally with wrong that does no harm.
Perhaps 'tis tender too and pretty
At each wild word to feel within
A sweet recoil of love and pity.
And what, if in a world of sin
(O sorrow and shame should this be true!)
Such giddiness of heart and brain
Comes seldom save from rage and pain,
So talks as it's most used to do.

SAMUEL TAYLOR COLERIDGE

A Birthday

My heart is like a singing bird
   Whose nest is in a watered shoot;
My heart is like an apple-tree
   Whose boughs are bent with thickset fruit;
My heart is like a rainbow shell
   That paddles in a halcyon sea;
My heart is gladder than all these
   Because my love is come to me.

Raise me a dais of silk and down;
   Hang it with vair and purple dyes;
Carve it in doves, and pomegranates,
   And peacocks with a hundred eyes;
Work it in gold and silver grapes,
   In leaves, and silver fleurs-de-lys;
Because the birthday of my life
   Is come, my love is come to me.

CHRISTINA ROSSETTI

From- 'Sohrab and Rustum'

AND night came down over the solemn waste,
And the two gazing hosts, and that sole pair,
And darken'd all; and a cold fog, with night,
Crept from the Oxus. Soon a hum arose,
As of a great assembly loos'd, and fires
Began to twinkle through the fog: for now
Both armies mov'd to camp and took their meal:
The Persians took it on the open sands
Southward; the Tartars by the river marge:
And Rustum and his son were left alone.
    But the majestic river floated on,
Out of the mist and hum of that low land,
Into the frosty starlight, and there mov'd,
Rejoicing, through the hushed Chorasmian waste,
Under the solitary moon: he flow'd
Right for the Polar Star, past Orgunjè,
Brimming, and bright, and large: then sands begin
To hem his watery march, and dam his streams,
And split his currents; that for many a league
The shorn and parcell'd Oxus strains along
Through beds of sand and matted rushy isles—
Oxus, forgetting the bright speed he had
In his high mountain cradle in Pamere,
A foil'd circuitous wanderer:—till at last
The long'd-for dash of waves is heard, and wide
His luminous home of waters opens, bright
And tranquil, from whose floor the new-bath'd stars
Emerge, and shine upon the Aral Sea.

MATTHEW ARNOLD

From- 'Henry V'

Once more unto the breach, dear friends, once more;
Or close the wall up with our English dead.
In peace there's nothing so becomes a man
As modest stillness and humility:
But when the blast of war blows in our ears,
Then imitate the action of the tiger;
Stiffen the sinews, summon up the blood,
Disguise fair nature with hard-favour'd rage;
Then lend the eye a terrible aspect;
Let it pry through the portage of the head
Like the brass cannon; let the brow o'erwhelm it
As fearfully as doth a galled rock
O'erhang and jutty his confounded base,
Swill'd with the wild and wasteful ocean.
Now set the teeth and stretch the nostril wide,
Hold hard the breath and bend up every spirit
To his full height. On, on, you noblest English,
Whose blood is fet from fathers of war-proof!
Fathers that, like so many Alexanders,
Have in these parts from morn to even fought,
And sheathed their swords for lack of argument:
Dishonour not your mothers; now attest
That those whom you call'd fathers did beget you.
Be copy now to men of grosser blood,
And teach them how to war. And you, good yeomen,
Whose limbs were made in England, show us here
The mettle of your pasture; let us swear
That you are worth your breeding; which I doubt not;
For there is none of you so mean and base,
That hath not noble lustre in your eyes.
I see you stand like greyhounds in the slips,
Straining upon the start. The game's afoot:
Follow your spirit, and upon this charge
Cry ' God for Harry, England, and Saint George! '

WILLIAM SHAKESPEARE

From-'Ulysses'

THERE lies the port; the vessel puffs her sail:
There gloom the dark broad seas. My mariners,
Souls that have toiled, and wrought, and thought with me—
That ever with a frolic welcome took
The thunder and the sunshine, and opposed
Free hearts, free foreheads—you and I are old;
Old age hath yet his honour and his toil;
Death closes all; but something ere the end,
Some work of noble note, may yet be done,
Not unbecoming men that strove with Gods.
The lights begin to twinkle from the rocks:
The long day wanes: the slow moon climbs: the deep
Moans round with many voices. Come, my friends,
'Tis not too late to seek a newer world.
Push off, and sitting well in order smite
The sounding furrows; for my purpose holds
To sail beyond the sunset, and the baths
Of all the western stars, until I die.
It may be that the gulfs will wash us down:
It may be we shall touch the Happy Isles,
And see the great Achilles, whom we knew.
Though much is taken, much abides; and though
We are not now that strength which in old days
Moved earth and heaven; that which we are, we are;
One equal temper of heroic hearts,
Made weak by time and fate, but strong in will
To strive, to seek, to find, and not to yield.

ALFRED, LORD TENNYSON

From-'The Eve of St. Agnes'

Then by the bed-side, where the faded moon
Made a dim, silver twilight, soft he set
A table, and, half anguish'd, threw thereon
A cloth of woven crimson, gold, and jet:—
O for some drowsy Morphean amulet!
The boisterous, midnight, festive clarion,
The kettle-drum, and far-heard clarinet,
Affray his ears, though but in dying tone:—
The hall door shuts again, and all the noise is gone.

And still she slept an azure-lidded sleep,
In blanched linen, smooth, and lavender'd,
While he from forth the closet brought a heap
Of candied apple, quince, and plum, and gourd;
With jellies soother than the creamy curd,
And lucent syrops, tinct with cinnamon;
Manna and dates, in argosy transferr'd
From Fez; and spiced dainties, every one,
From silken Samarcand to cedar'd Lebanon.

These delicates he heap'd with glowing hand
On golden dishes and in baskets bright
Of wreathed silver: sumptuous they stand
In the retired quiet of the night,
Filling the chilly room with perfume light.—
'And now, my love, my seraph fair, awake!
'Thou art my heaven, and I thine eremite:
'Open thine eyes for meek St. Agnes' sake,
'Or I shall drowse beside thee, so my soul doth ache.'

JOHN KEATS

Runnymede

(Magna Charta, June 15, 1215)

At Runnymede, at Runnymede,
  What say the reeds at Runnymede?
The lissom reeds that give and take,
That bend so far, but never break.
They keep the sleepy Thames awake
  With tales of John at Runnymede.

At Runnymede, at Runnymede,
  Oh hear the reeds at Runnymede:—
'You mustn't sell, delay, deny,
A freeman's right or liberty,
It wakes the stubborn Englishry,
  We saw 'em roused at Runnymede!

'When through our ranks the Barons came,
With little thought of praise or blame,
But resolute to play the game,
  They lumbered up to Runnymede;
And there they launched in solid line,
The first attack on Right Divine—
The curt, uncompromising "Sign!"
  That settled John at Runnymede.

'At Runnymede, at Runnymede,
Your rights were won at Runnymede!
No freeman shall be fined or bound,
  Or dispossessed of freehold ground,
Except by lawful judgment found
And passed upon him by his peers!
Forget not, after all these years,
  The Charter signed at Runnymede.'

And still when Mob or Monarch lays
Too rude a hand on English ways,
The whisper wakes, the shudder plays,
  Across the reeds at Runnymede.
And Thames, that knows the moods of kings
And crowds and priests and suchlike things,
Rolls deep and dreadful as he brings
  Their warning down from Runnymede!

RUDYARD KIPLING

Turtle Soup

Beautiful Soup, so rich and green,
Waiting in a hot tureen!
Who for such dainties would not stoop?
Soup of the evening, beautiful Soup!
Soup of the evening, beautiful Soup!
   Beau - ootiful Soo - oop!
   Beau - ootiful Soo - oop!
Soo - oop of the e - e - evening,
   Beautiful, beautiful Soup!

Beautiful Soup! Who cares for fish,
Game, or any other dish?
Who would not give all else for two
Pennyworth only of beautiful Soup?
   Beau - ootiful Soo - oop!
   Beau - ootiful Soo - oop!
Soo - oop of the e - e - evening,
   Beautiful, beauti - FUL SOUP!

LEWIS CARROLL

I SAW a peacock with a fiery tail
I saw a blazing comet drop down hail
I saw a cloud with ivy circled round
I saw a sturdy oak creep on the ground
I saw a pismire swallow up a whale
I saw a raging sea brim full of ale
I saw a venice glass sixteen foot deep
I saw a well full of men's tears that weep
I saw their eyes all in a flame of fire
I saw a house as big as the moon and higher
I saw the sun even in the midst of night
I saw the man that saw this wondrous sight.

OLD NURSERY RHYME

The Owl and the Pussy-cat

THE Owl and the Pussy-Cat went to sea
  In a beautiful pea-green boat,
They took some honey, and plenty of money
  Wrapped up in a five-pound note,
The Owl looked up to the stars above,
  And sang to a small guitar,
'O lovely Pussy! O Pussy, my love,
  What a beautiful Pussy you are,
      You are,
      You are!
  What a beautiful Pussy you are!'

Pussy said to the Owl, 'You elegant fowl!
  How charmingly sweet you sing!
O let us be married! too long we have tarried:
  But what shall we do for a ring?'
They sailed away for a year and a day,
  To the land where the Bong-tree grows,
And there in a wood a Piggy-wig stood,
  With a ring at the end of his nose,
      His nose,
      His nose,
  With a ring at the end of his nose.

'Dear Pig, are you willing to sell for one shilling
 Your ring?' Said the Piggy, 'I will.'
So they took it away, and were married next day
 By the Turkey who lives on the hill.
They dinèd on mince, and slices of quince,
 Which they ate with a runcible spoon;
And hand in hand, on the edge of the sand,
 They danced by the light of the moon,
  The moon,
  The moon,
They danced by the light of the moon.

EDWARD LEAR

From- 'Tamburlaine The Great'

NATURE, that fram'd us of four elements
Warring within our breasts for regiment,
Doth teach us all to have aspiring minds:
Our souls, whose faculties can comprehend
The wondrous architecture of the world,
And measure every wandering planet's course,
Still climbing after knowledge infinite,
And always moving as the restless spheres,
Wills us to wear ourselves and never rest,
Until we reach the ripest fruit of all,
That perfect bliss and sole felicity,
The sweet fruition of an earthly crown.

CHRISTOPHER MARLOWE

Humpty Dumpty's Poem

In winter, when the fields are white,
I sing this song for your delight—

In spring, when woods are getting green,
I'll try and tell you what I mean.

In summer, when the days are long,
Perhaps you'll understand the song:

In autumn, when the leaves are brown,
Take pen and ink and write it down.

I sent a message to the fish:
I told them 'This is what I wish.'

The little fishes of the sea,
They sent an answer back to me.

The little fishes' answer was
'We cannot do it, Sir, because—'

I sent to them again to say
'It will be better to obey.'

The fishes answered with a grin,
'Why, what a temper you are in!'

I told them once, I told them twice:
They would not listen to advice.

I took a kettle large and new,
Fit for the deed I had to do.

My heart went hop, my heart went thump;
I filled the kettle at the pump.

Then someone came to me and said,
'The little fishes are in bed.'

I said to him, I said it plain,
'Then you must wake them up again.'

I said it very loud and clear;
I went and shouted in his ear.

But he was very stiff and proud;
He said, 'You needn't shout so loud!'

And he was very proud and stiff;
He said, 'I'd go and wake them if—'

I took a corkscrew from the shelf:
I went to wake them up myself.

And when I found the door was locked,
I pulled and pushed and kicked and knocked.

And when I found the door was shut,
I tried to turn the handle, but—

LEWIS CARROLL

From-'A Midsummer Night's Dream'

Now the hungry lion roars
  And the wolf behowls the moon;
Whilst the heavy ploughman snores,
  All with weary task foredone.
Now the wasted brands do glow,
  Whilst the screech-owl, screeching loud,
Puts the wretch that lies in woe
  In remembrance of a shroud.
Now it is the time of night,
  That the graves, all gaping wide,
Every one lets forth his sprite,
  In the church-way paths to glide:
And we fairies, that do run
  By the triple Hecate's team,
From the presence of the sun,
  Following darkness like a dream,
Now are frolic: not a mouse
Shall disturb this hallowed house:
I am sent with broom before,
To sweep the dust behind the door.

WILLIAM SHAKESPEARE

WHEN I was a little boy I lived by myself,
And all the bread and cheese I got I laid upon a shelf;
The rats and the mice they made such a strife,
I had to go to London-town and buy me a wife.

The streets were so broad and the lanes were so
  narrow,
I was forced to bring my wife home in a wheelbarrow.
The wheelbarrow broke and my wife had a fall,
Farewell wheelbarrow, little wife and all.

OLD NURSERY RHYME

From-'A Winter's Tale'

LAWN as white as driven snow;
Cypress black as e'er was crow;
Gloves as sweet as damask roses;
Masks for faces and for noses;
Bugle bracelet, necklace amber,
Perfume for a lady's chamber;
Golden quoifs and stomachers,
For my lads to give their dears;
Pins and poking-sticks of steel,
What maids lack from head to heel:
Come buy of me, come; come buy, come buy;
Buy, lads, or else your lasses cry
Come buy.

WILLIAM SHAKESPEARE

The Bees' Song

T HOUSANDZ of thornz there be
On the Rozez where gozez
The Zebra of Zee:
Sleek, striped, and hairy,
The steed of the Fairy
Princess of Zee.

Heavy with blossomz be
The Rozez that growzez
In the thicketz of Zee.
Where grazez the Zebra,
Marked Abracadeeebra
Of the Princess of Zee.

And he nozez the poziez
Of the Rozez that growzez
So luvez'm and free,
With an eye, dark, and wary,
In search of a Fairy,
Whose Rozez he knowzez
Were not honied for he,
But to breathe a sweet incense
To solace the Princess
Of far-away Zee.

WALTER DE LA MARE

The Lady and the Bear

A LADY came to a Bear by a stream.
'O why are you fishing that way?
Tell me, dear Bear there by the Stream,
Why are you fishing that way?'

'I am what is known as a Biddly Bear,—
That's why I'm fishing this way.
We Biddly's are Pee-culiar Bears.
And so,—I'm fishing this way.

And besides, it seems there's a Law:
A most, most exactious Law
Says a Bear
Doesn't dare
Doesn't dare
Doesn't DARE
Use a Hook or a Line,
Or an old piece of Twine,
Not even the end of his Claw, Claw, Claw,
Not even the end of his Claw.
Yes, a Bear has to fish with his Paw, Paw, Paw.
A Bear has to fish with his Paw.'

'O it's Wonderful how with a flick of your Wrist,
You can fish out a fish, out a fish, out a fish,
If *I* were a fish I just couldn't resist
You, when you are fishing that way, that way,
When you are fishing that way.'

And at that the Lady slipped from the Bank
And fell in the Stream still clutching a Plank,
But the Bear just sat there until she Sank;
As he went on fishing his way, his way,
As he went on fishing his way.

THEODORE ROETHKE

Gus: The Theatre Cat

Gus is the Cat at the Theatre Door.
His name, as I ought to have told you before,
Is really Asparagus. That's such a fuss
To pronounce, that we usually call him just Gus.
His coat's very shabby, he's thin as a rake,
And he suffers from palsy that makes his paw shake.
Yet he was, in his youth, quite the smartest of Cats—
But no longer a terror to mice and to rats.
For he isn't the Cat that he was in his prime;
Though his name was quite famous, he says, in its time.
And whenever he joins his friends at their club
(Which takes place at the back of the neighbouring pub)
He loves to regale them, if someone else pays,
With anecdotes drawn from his palmiest days.
For he once was a Star of the highest degree—
He has acted with Irving, he's acted with Tree.
And he likes to relate his success on the Halls,
Where the Gallery once gave him seven cat-calls.
But his grandest creation, as he loves to tell,
Was Firefrorefiddle, the Fiend of the Fell.

'I have played,' so he says, 'every possible part,
And I used to know seventy speeches by heart.
I'd extemporize back-chat, I knew how to gag,
And I knew how to let the cat out of the bag.
I knew how to act with my back and my tail;
With an hour of rehearsal, I never could fail.
I'd a voice that would soften the hardest of hearts,

Whether I took the lead, or in character parts.
I have sat by the bedside of poor Little Nell;
When the Curfew was rung, then I swung on the bell.
In the Pantomime season I never fell flat,
And I once understudied Dick Whittington's Cat.
But my grandest creation, as history will tell,
Was Firefrorefiddle, the Fiend of the Fell.'

Then, if someone will give him a toothful of gin,
He will tell how he once played a part in *East Lynne*.
At a Shakespeare performance he once walked on pat,
When some actor suggested the need for a cat.
He once played a Tiger—could do it again—
Which an Indian Colonel pursued down a drain.
And he thinks that he still can, much better than most,
Produce blood-curdling noises to bring on the Ghost.
And he once crossed the stage on a telegraph wire,
To rescue a child when a house was on fire.
And he says: 'Now, these kittens, they do not get
    trained
As we did in the days when Victoria reigned.
They never get drilled in a regular troupe,
And they think they are smart, just to jump through a
    hoop.'
And he'll say, as he scratches himself with his claws,
'Well, the Theatre's certainly not what it was.
These modern productions are all very well,
But there's nothing to equal, from what I hear tell,
              That moment of mystery
              When I made history
As Firefrorefiddle, the Fiend of the Fell.'

T. S. ELIOT

The Lobster Quadrille

Will you walk a little faster?' said a whiting to a
  snail.
'There's a porpoise close behind us, and he's treading
  on my tail.
See how eagerly the lobsters and the turtles all advance!
They are waiting on the shingle—will you come and
  join the dance?
  Will you, won't you, will you, won't you, will you
    join the dance?
  Will you, won't you, will you, won't you, won't
    you join the dance?

'You can really have no notion how delightful it will be,
When they take us up and throw us, with the lobsters,
  out to sea!'
But the snail replied 'Too far, too far!' and gave a
  look askace—
Said he thanked the whiting kindly, but he would not
  join the dance.
  Would not, could not, would not, could not, would
    not join the dance.
  Would not, could not, would not, could not, could
    not join the dance.

'What matters it how far we go?' his scaly friend
  replied.
'There is another shore, you know, upon the other side.
The further off from England the nearer is to France—
Then turn not pale, beloved snail, but come and join
  the dance.
  Will you, won't you, will you, won't you, will you
    join the dance?
  Will you, won't you, will you, won't you, won't you
    join the dance?'

LEWIS CARROLL

Street Criers

(written for music)

WHEN Poll stays here, her Jack goes there,
   To earn their provender;
Her cries are all in Bethnal Green—
   'Sweet Lavender! Sweet Lavender!
Who'll buy Sweet Lavender?'

And oft she wonders if her Jack
   Enjoys a man's success;
Who cries on top of Stamford Hill—
   'Young Watercress! Young Watercress!
Who'll buy Young Watercress?'

W. H. DAVIES

Cock Robin

WHO killed Cock Robin?
I, said the Sparrow,
With my bow and arrow,
I killed Cock Robin.

Who saw him die?
I, said the Fly,
With my little eye,
I saw him die.

Who caught his blood?
I, said the Fish,
With my little dish
I caught his blood.

Who'll make the shroud?
I, said the Beetle,
With my thread and
 needle,
I'll make the shroud.

Who'll dig his grave?
I, said the Owl,
With my pick and shovel,
I'll dig his grave.

Who'll be the parson?
I, said the Rook,
With my little book,
I'll be the parson.

Who'll be the clerk?
I, said the Lark,
If it's not in the dark,
I'll be the clerk.

Who'll carry the link?
I, said the Linnet,
I'll fetch it in a minute,
I'll carry the link.

Who'll be chief mourner?
I, said the Dove,
I'll mourn for my love,
I'll be chief mourner.

Who'll carry the coffin?
I, said the Kite,
If it's not through the
 night,
I'll carry the coffin.

Who'll bear the pall?
We, said the Wren,
Both the cock and the
   hen,
We'll bear the pall.

Who'll sing a psalm?
I, said the Thrush,
As she sat on a bush,
I'll sing a psalm.

Who'll toll the bell?
I, said the Bull,
Because I can pull,
I'll toll the bell.

All the birds of the air
Fell a-sighing and a-sobbing,
When they heard the bell
   toll
For poor Cock Robin.

OLD NURSERY RHYME

Epigram

As Thomas was cudgell'd one day by his wife,
He took to the street, and fled for his life:
Tom's three dearest friends came by in the squabble,
And saved him at once from the shrew and the rabble;
Then ventured to give him some sober advice—
But Tom is a person of honour so nice,
Too wise to take counsel, too proud to take warning,
That he sent to all three a challenge next morning.
Three duels he fought, thrice ventur'd his life;
Went home, and was cudgell'd again by his wife.

JONATHAN SWIFT

There was a Naughty Boy

THERE was a naughty boy,
And a naughty boy was he.
He ran away to Scotland,
The people for to see.
　　Then he found
　　　　That the ground
　　　　Was as hard,
　　　　That a yard
　　　　Was as long,
　　　　That a song
　　　　Was as merry,
　　　　That a cherry
　　　　Was as red,
　　　　That lead
　　　　Was as weighty,
　　　　That four-score
　　　　Was as eighty,
　　　　That a door
　　　　Was as wooden
　　　　As in England.
So he stood in his shoes,
　　And he wondered,
　　He wondered,
He stood in his shoes
　　And he wondered.

JOHN KEATS

Eldorado

Gaily bedight,
A gallant knight,
In sunshine and in shadow,
Had journeyed long,
Singing a song,
In search of Eldorado.

But he grew old—
This knight so bold—
And o'er his heart a shadow
Fell as he found
No spot of ground
That looked like Eldorado.

And, as his strength
Failed him at length,
He met a pilgrim shadow:
'Shadow,' said he,
'Where can it be,
This land of Eldorado?'

'Over the mountains
Of the moon,
Down the valley of the shadow,
Ride, boldly ride,'
The shade replied,
'If you seek for Eldorado.'

EDGAR ALLAN POE

Pirate Story

THREE of us afloat in the meadow by the swing,
  Three of us aboard in the basket on the lea.
Winds are in the air, they are blowing in the spring,
  And waves are on the meadows like the waves there
    are at sea.

Where shall we adventure, to-day that we're afloat,
  Wary of the weather and steering by a star?
Shall it be to Africa, a-steering of the boat,
  To Providence, or Babylon, or off to Malabar?

Hi! but here's a squadron a-rowing on the sea—
  Cattle on the meadow a-charging with a roar!
Quick, and we'll escape them, they're as mad as they
    can be.
  The wicket is the harbour and the garden is the shore.

ROBERT LOUIS STEVENSON

Now Philippa is Gone

Now Philippa is gone, that so divinely
Could strum and sing, and is rufus and gay,
Have we the heart to sing, or at midday
Dive under Trotton Bridge? We shall only
Doze in the yellow spikenard by the wood
And take our tea and melons in the shade.

ANNE RIDLER

George

*who played with a Dangerous Toy, and suffered
a Catastrophe of considerable Dimensions*

WHEN George's Grandmamma was told
That George had been as good as Gold,
She Promised in the Afternoon
To buy him an *immense* BALLOON.
And so she did; but when it came,
It got into the candle flame,
And being of a dangerous sort
Exploded with a loud report!
The Lights went out! The Windows broke!
The Room was filled with reeking smoke.
And in the darkness shrieks and yells
Were mingled with Electric Bells,
And falling masonry and groans,
And crunching, as of broken bones,
And dreadful shrieks, when, worst of all,
The House itself began to fall!
It tottered, shuddering to and fro,
Then crashed into the street below—
Which happened to be Savile Row.

When Help arrived, among the Dead
Were Cousin Mary, Little Fred,
The Footmen (both of them), The Groom,
The man that cleaned the Billiard-Room,

The Chaplain, and The Still-Room Maid.
And I am dreadfully afraid
That Monsieur Champignon, the Chef,
Will now be permanently deaf—
And both his Aides are much the same;
While George, who was in part to blame,
Received, you will regret to hear,
A nasty lump behind the ear.
MORAL
 The moral is that little Boys
 Should not be given dangerous Toys.

HILAIRE BELLOC

OLD woman, old woman, shall we go a-shearing?
Speak a little louder, sir, I'm very thick of hearing.
Old woman, old woman, shall I love you dearly?
Thank you very kindly, sir, now I hear you clearly.

OLD NURSERY RHYME

'When Cats Run Home'

WHEN cats run home and light is come,
　And dew is cold upon the ground,
And the far-off stream is dumb,
　And the whirring sail goes round,
　And the whirring sail goes round;
　　Alone and warming his five wits,
　　The white owl in the belfry sits.

When merry milkmaids click the latch,
　And rarely smells the new-mown hay,
And the cock hath sung beneath the thatch
　Twice or thrice his roundelay,
　Twice or thrice his roundelay;
　　Alone and warming his five wits,
　　The white owl in the belfry sits.

ALFRED, LORD TENNYSON

The Bell-man

From noise of Scare-fires rest ye free,
From Murders—*Benedicite*.
From all mischances, that may fright
Your pleasing slumbers in the night:
Mercie secure ye all, and keep
The Goblin from ye, while ye sleep.
Past one aclock, and almost two,
My Masters all, *Good day to you*!

ROBERT HERRICK

Bermudas

Where the remote Bermudas ride,
In the ocean's bosom unespied,
From a small boat that rowed along,
The listening winds received this song:

'What shall we do but sing His praise,
That led us through the watery maze
Unto an isle so long unknown,
And yet far kinder than our own?
Where He the huge sea-monsters wracks,
That lift the deep upon their backs;
He lands us on a grassy stage,
Safe from the storms, and prelate's rage.
He gave us this eternal spring,
Which here enamels everything,
And sends the fowls to us in care,
On daily visits though the air;
He hangs in shades the orange bright,
Like golden lamps in a green night,
And does in the pomegranates close
Jewels more rich than Ormus shows;
He makes the figs our mouths to meet,
And throws the melons at our feet;
But apples plants of such a price,
No tree could ever bear them twice;
With cedars chosen by His hand,
From Lebanon, He stores the land,
And makes the hollow seas, that roar,
Proclaim the ambergris on shore;
He cast (of which we rather boast)
The Gospel's pearl upon our coast,
And in these rocks for us did frame
A temple where to sound His name.

Oh! let our voice His praise exalt,
Till it arrive at Heaven's vault,
Which, thence (perhaps) rebounding, may
Echo beyond the Mexique Bay.'

Thus sung they, in the English boat,
An holy and a cheerful note;
And all the way, to guide their chime,
With falling oars they kept the time.

ANDREW MARVELL

In marble halls as white as milk,
Lined with a skin as soft as silk,
Within a fountain crystal-clear,
A golden apple doth appear.
No doors there are to this stronghold,
Yet thieves break in and steal the gold.

OLD NURSERY RHYME

T HERE was a king met a king
   In a narrow lane;
Said the king to the king,
   Where have you been?
I have been a hunting
   The buck and the doe.
Will you lend me your dog?
   Yes, I will do so;
Call upon him, call upon him.
   What is his name?
I have told you twice
   And won't tell you again.

OLD NURSERY RHYME

Miranda's song

My Dear One is mine as mirrors are lonely,
As the poor and sad are real to the good king,
And the high green hill sits always by the sea.

Up jumped the Black Man behind the elder tree,
Turned a somersault and ran away waving;
My Dear One is mine as mirrors are lonely.

The Witch gave a squawk: her venomous body
Melted into light as water leaves a spring
And the high green hill sits always by the sea.

At his crossroads, too, the Ancient prayed for me;
Down his wasted cheeks tears of joy were running:
My Dear One is mine as mirrors are lonely.

He kissed me awake, and no-one was sorry;
The sun shone on sails, eyes, pebbles, anything,
And the high green hill sits always by the sea.

So, to remember our changing garden, we
Are linked as children in a circle dancing:
My Dear One is mine as mirrors are lonely,
And the high green hill sits always by the sea.

W. H. AUDEN

Dream-Pedlary

If there were dreams to sell,
  What would you buy?
Some cost a passing bell;
  Some a light sigh,
That shakes from Life's fresh crown
Only a rose-leaf down.
If there were dreams to sell,
Merry and sad to tell,
And the crier rang the bell,
  What would you buy?

A cottage lone and still,
  With bowers nigh,
Shadowy, my woes to still,
  Until I die.
Such pearl from Life's fresh crown
Fain would I shake me down.
Were dreams to have at will,
This would best heal my ill,
  This would I buy.

THOMAS LOVELL BEDDOES

The End of the Road

From – 'The Path to Rome'

IN these boots and with this staff
Two hundred leaguers and a half
Walked I, went I, paced I, tripped I,
Marched I, held I, skelped I, slipped I,
Pushed I, panted, swung and dashed I;
Picked I, forded, swam and splashed I,
Strolled I, climbed I, crawled and scrambled,
Dropped and dipped I, ranged and rambled;
Plodded I, hobbled I, trudged and tramped I,
And in lonely spinnies camped I,
Lingered, loitered, limped and crept I,
Clambered, halted, stepped and leapt I,
Slowly sauntered, roundly strode I,
And . . .
Let me not conceal it . . . rode I.

(For who but critics could complain
Of 'riding' in a railway train?)

Across the vallies and the high land,
With all the world on either hand,
Drinking when I had a mind to,
Singing when I felt inclined to;
Nor ever turned my face to home
Till I had slaked my heart at Rome.

HILAIRE BELLOC

From- 'The Lady's not for Burning'

Why do they call me a witch?
Remember my father was an alchemist.
I live alone, preferring loneliness
To the companionable suffocation of an aunt.
I still amuse myself with simple experiments
In my father's laboratory. Also I speak
French to my poodle. Then you must know
I have a peacock which on Sundays
Dines with me indoors. Not long ago
A new little serving maid carrying the food
Heard its cry, dropped everything and ran,
Never to come back, and told all whom she met
That the devil was dining with me.

CHRISTOPHER FRY

THE Lord possessed me in the beginning of his ways, before he made anything, from the beginning.
I was set up from eternity, and of old, before the earth was made. The depths were not as yet, and I was already conceived; neither had the fountains of waters as yet sprung out; the mountains with their huge bulk had not as yet been established: before the hills I was brought forth.
He had not yet made the earth, nor the rivers, nor the poles of the world. When he prepared the heavens, I was there; when with a certain law and compass he enclosed the depths; when he established the sky above, and poised the fountains of waters;
When he compassed the sea with its bounds, and set a law to the waters that they should not pass their limits; when he balanced the foundations of the earth;
I was with him, forming all things, and was delighted every day, playing before him at all times, playing in the world: and my delight is to be with the children.

PROVERBS VIII 22-35

From-'Hymn on the Morning of Christ's Nativity'

It was the Winter wild,
While the Heaven-born child,
   All meanly wrapt in the rude manger lies;
Nature in awe to him
Had doffed her gawdy trim,
   With her great Master so to sympathize:
It was no season then for her
To wanton with the Sun, her lusty Paramour.

Only with speeches fair
She woos the gentle Air
   To hide her guilty front with innocent Snow,
And on her naked shame,
Pollute with sinful blame,
   The Saintly Veil of Maiden white to throw,
Confounded, that her Maker's eyes
Should look so near upon her foul deformities.

But he her fears to cease,
Sent down the meek-eyed Peace,
   She crowned with Olive green, came softly sliding
Down through the turning sphere
His ready Harbinger,
   With Turtle wings the amorous clouds dividing,
And waving wide her myrtle wand,
She strikes a universal peace through sea and land.

No War, or Battle's sound
Was heard the World around:
  The idle spear and shield were high uphung;
The hooked Chariot stood
Unstained with hostile blood,
  The trumpet spake not to the armed throng,
And Kings sat still with awful eye,
As if they surely knew their sovereign Lord was by.

But peaceful was the night
Wherein the Prince of light
  His reign of peace upon the earth began:
The Winds with wonder whist,
Smoothly the waters kissed,
  Whispering new joys to the mild Ocean,
Who now hath quite forgot to rave,
While Birds of Calm sit brooding on the charmed wave.

JOHN MILTON

Aɴᴅ she brought forth her first-born son, and wrapped him up in swaddling clothes, and laid him in a manger: because there was no room for them in the inn.

And there were in the same country shepherds watching, and keeping the night-watches over their flock.

And behold an angel of the Lord stood by them, and the brightness of God shone round about them, and they feared with a great fear.

And the angel said to them: Fear not; for behold I bring you good tidings of great joy that shall be to all the people:

For this day is born to you a SAVIOUR, who is Christ the Lord, in the city of David.

And this shall be a sign unto you. You shall find the infant wrapped in swaddling clothes, and laid in a manger.

And suddenly there was with the angel a multitude of the heavenly army, praising God, and saying:

Glory to God in the highest: and on earth peace to men of good will. And it came to pass, after the angels departed from them into Heaven, the shepherds said one to another, Let us go over to Bethlehem, and let us see this word that is come to pass, which the Lord hath showed to us. And they came with haste: and they found Mary and Joseph, and the infant lying in the manger.

And seeing, they understood of the word that had been spoken to them concerning this child.

And all that heard wondered: and at those things that were told them by the shepherds.

But Mary kept all these words, pondering them in her heart. And the shepherds returned, glorifying and praising God, for all the things they had heard, and seen, as it was told unto them.

LUKE II 7-20

From-'The Cherry-tree Carol'

As Joseph was a-walking,
  He heard an angel sing:
'This night shall be born
  Our heavenly King.

'He neither shall be born
  In housen nor in hall,
Nor in the place of Paradise,
  But in an ox's stall.

'He neither shall be clothèd
  In purple nor in pall,
But all in fair linen,
  As were babies all.

'He neither shall be rock'd
  In silver nor in gold,
But in a wooden cradle
  That rocks on the mould.

'He neither shall be christen'd
  In white wine nor red,
But with fair spring water
  With which we were christenèd.

'Then Mary took her young son
    And set him on her knee;
"I pray thee now, dear child,
    Tell how this world shall be."—

'O I shall be as dead, mother,
    As the stones in the wall;
O the stones in the street, mother,
    Shall mourn for me all.

'And upon a Wednesday
    My vow I will make,
And upon Good Friday
    My death I will take.

'Upon Easter-day, mother,
    My uprising shall be;
O the sun and the moon, mother,
    Shall both rise with me!'

ANONYMOUS

Love

Love bade me welcome; yet my soul drew back,
  Guilty of dust and sin.
But quick-ey'd Love, observing me grow slack
  From my first entrance in,
Drew nearer to me, sweetly questioning
  If I lack'd anything.

'A guest,' I answer'd, 'worthy to be here:'
  Love said, 'You shall be he.'
'I, the unkind, ungrateful? Ah, my dear,
  I cannot look on Thee.'
Love took my hand and smiling did reply,
  'Who made the eyes but I?'

'Truth, Lord; but I have marr'd them; let my shame
  Go where it doth deserve.'
'And know you not,' says Love, 'Who bore the blame?'
  'My dear, then I will serve.'
'You must sit down,' says Love, 'and taste My meat.'
  So I did sit and eat.

GEORGE HERBERT

'I Heard an Angel Singing'

I HEARD an angel singing
When the day was springing:
'Mercy, Pity, Peace
Is the world's release.'

Thus he sung all day
Over the new-mown hay,
Till the sun went down,
And haycocks looked brown.

I heard a Devil curse
Over the heath and the furze:
'Mercy could be no more
If there was nobody poor,

'And Pity no more could be,
If all were as happy as we.'
At his curse the sun went down,
And the heavens gave a frown.

Down poured the heavy rain
Over the new-reaped grain;
And Misery's increase
Is Mercy, Pity, Peace.

WILLIAM BLAKE

To the Spring

EARTH now is green, and heaven is blue,
Lively spring which makes all new,
Jolly spring doth enter:
Sweet young sunbeams do subdue
Angry, agéd winter.

Blasts are mild, and seas are calm,
Every meadow flows with balm,
The earth wears all her riches;
Harmonious birds sing such a psalm
As ear and heart bewitches.

Reserve, sweet spring, this nymph of ours
Eternal garlands of thy flowers,
Green garlands never wasting;
In her shall last our State's fair spring,
Now and for ever flourishing,
As long as heaven is lasting.

SIR JOHN DAVIES

Poverty

As in the house I sate
  Alone and desolate,
No creature but the fire and I,
The chimney and the stool, I lift mine eye
    Up to the wall,
    And in the silent hall
      Saw nothing mine
But some few cups and dishes shine,
The table and the wooden stools
    Where people used to dine:
    A painted cloth there was
Wherein some ancient story wrought
A little entertain'd my thought
Which light discovered through the glass.

    I wonder'd much to see
    That all my wealth should be
  Confin'd in such a little room,
Yet hope for more I scarcely durst presume.
    It griev'd me sore
    That such a scanty store
      Should be my all:
For I forgot my ease and health,
Nor did I think of hands or eyes,
    Nor soul nor body prize;
    I neither thought the sun,
Nor moon, nor stars, nor people, *mine*,
Though they did round about me shine;
And therefore was I quite undone.

Some greater things I thought
　　Must needs for me be wrought,
　Which till my craving mind could see
I ever should lament my poverty:
　　I fain would have
　Whatever bounty gave;
　　Nor could there be
Without, or love or deity:
For should not he be infinite
　　Whose hand created me?
　　Ten thousand absent things
Did vex my poor and wanting mind,
Which, till I be no longer blind,
Let me not see the King of Kings.

THOMAS TRAHERNE

The Ladybird

LADYBIRD! Ladybird! Where art thou gone?
Ere the daisy was open or the rose it was spread
On the cabbage flower early thy scarlet wings shone,
I saw thee creep off to the tulip's bed.
Ladybird! Ladybird! Where art thou flown?
Thou wert here in the morning before the sun shone.

Just now up the bole o' the damson tree
You pass the gold lichen and got to the grey—
Ladybird! Ladybird! Where can you be?
You climb up the tulips and then fly away.
You crept up the flowers while I plucked them just now
And crept to the top and then flew from the flowers.
O sleep not so high as the damson tree bough,
But come from the dew i' the eldern tree bower.

Here's lavendar trees that would hide a lone mouse
And lavendar cotton wi' buttons o' gold,
And bushes o' lad's love as dry as a house,
Here's red pinks and daisies so sweet to behold.
Ladybird! Ladybird! Come to thy nest,
Thy gold bed's i' the rose o' the sweet brier tree,
Wi' rose coloured curtains to pleasure thee best;
Come, Ladybird, back to thy garden and me.

JOHN CLARE

Abou Ben Adhem

ABOU BEN ADHEM (may his tribe increase!)
Awoke one night from a deep dream of peace,
And saw, within the moonlight in his room,
Making it rich, and like a lily in bloom,
An angel writing in a book of gold:—
Exceeding peace had made Ben Adhem bold,
And to the presence in the room he said,
    'What writest thou?' The vision rais'd its head,
And with a look made of all sweet accord,
Answer'd, 'The names of those who love the Lord.'
    'And is mine one?' said Abou. 'Nay, not so,'
Replied the angel. Abou spoke more low,
But cheerly still; and said, 'I pray thee, then,
Write me as one that loves his fellow men.'
    The angel wrote, and vanish'd. The next night
It came again with a great wakening light,
And show'd the names whom love of God had blest,
And lo! Ben Adhem's name led all the rest.

LEIGH HUNT

The Pulley

WHEN God at first made man,
Having a glass of blessings standing by;
  'Let us', said he, 'pour on him all we can:
Let the world's riches, which dispersèd lie,
  Contract into a span.'

  So strength first made a way;
Then beauty flowed, then wisdom, honour, pleasure:
  When almost all was out, God made a stay,
Perceiving that alone of all his treasure
  Rest in the bottom lay.

  'For if I should', said he,
'Bestow this jewel also on my creature,
  He would adore my gifts instead of me,
And rest in Nature, not the God of Nature:
  So both should losers be.

  'Yet let him keep the rest,
But keep them with repining restlessness:
  Let him be rich and weary, that at least
If goodness lead him not, yet weariness
  May toss him to my breast.'

GEORGE HERBERT

Echo

Nothing is lost, sweet self,
Nothing is ever lost.
The unspoken word
Is not exhausted but can be heard.
Music that stains
The silence remains
O echo is everywhere, the unbeckonable bird!

LAWRENCE DURRELL

From-'Friends Departed'

They are all gone into the world of light!
    And I alone sit ling'ring here;
Their very memory is fair and bright,
    And my sad thoughts doth clear.

It glows and glitters in my cloudy breast,
    Like stars upon some gloomy grove,
Or those fair beams in which this hill is drest
    After the sun's remove.

I see them walking in an air of glory,
    Whose light doth trample on my days:
My days, which are at best but dull and hoary,
    Mere glimmerings and decays.

He that hath found some fledg'd bird's nest may know,
    At that first sight, if the bird be flown;
But what fair well or grove he sings in now,
    That is to him unknown.

And yet as Angels in some brighter dreams
    Call to the soul when man doth sleep:
So some strange thoughts transcend our wonted themes,
    And in to glory peep.

HENRY VAUGHAN

From-'Psalm 103'

THOU waterest the hills from the heights above: the
earth shall be filled with the fruit of thy works,
Bringing forth grass for cattle: and herb for the service
of men.
That thou mayest bring bread out of the earth: and
that wine may cheer the heart of man.
To make the face cheerful with oil: and that bread
may strengthen man's heart.
The trees of the field shall be filled, and the cedars of
Libanus which he hath planted: there the sparrows
shall make their nests.
The highest of them is the home of the heron: the
high hills are a refuge for the harts, and the rocks for
the conies.
He hath made the moon for seasons: the sun knoweth
his going down.
Thou hast appointed darkness, and it is night: wherein
all the beasts of the woods shall come forth.
The young lions roaring after their prey, and seeking
their meat from God.
The sun ariseth, and they are gathered together: and
they shall lie down in their dens.
Man shall go forth to his work: and to his labour until
the evening.

From- 'The Blessed Virgin
Compared to the Air We Breathe'

I say that we are wound
With mercy round and round
As if with air: the same
Is Mary, more by name.
She, wild web, wondrous robe,
Mantles the guilty globe,
Since God has let dispense
Her prayers his providence:
Nay, more than almoner,
The sweet alms' self is her
And men are meant to share
Her life as life does air.
   If I have understood,
She holds high motherhood
Towards all our ghostly good
And plays in grace her part
About man's beating heart,
Laying, like air's fine flood,
The deathdance in his blood;
Yet no part but what will
Be Christ our Saviour still.
Of her flesh he took flesh:

He does take fresh and fresh,
Though much the mystery how,
Not flesh but spirit now
And makes, O marvellous!
New Nazareths in us,
Where she shall yet conceive
Him, morning, noon, and eve;
New Bethlems, and he born
There, evening, noon, and morn—
Bethlem or Nazareth,
Men here may draw like breath
More Christ and baffle death;
Who, born so, comes to be
New self and nobler me
In each one and each one
More makes, when all is done,
Both God's and Mary's Son.

GERARD MANLEY HOPKINS

From-'The Apocalypse'

And I saw heaven opened, and behold a white horse: and he that sat upon him was called Faithful and True, and with justice doth he judge and fight.

And his eyes were as a flame of fire, and on his head were many diadems, and he had a name written, which no man knoweth but himself.

And he was clothed with a garment sprinkled with blood: and his name is called, THE WORD OF GOD.

And the armies that are in heaven followed him on white horses, clothed in fine linen white and clean.

And out of his mouth proceedeth a sharp two-edged sword, that with it he may strike the nations. And he shall rule them with a rod of iron: and he treadeth the wine-press of the fierceness of the wrath of God the Almighty.

And he hath on his garment and on his thigh written: KING OF KINGS AND LORD OF LORDS.

And I saw an angel standing in the sun, and he cried with a loud voice, saying to all the birds that did fly through the midst of heaven: Come, gather yourselves together to the great supper of God:

That you may eat the flesh of kings, and the flesh of tribunes, and the flesh of mighty men, and the flesh of horses, and of them that sit on them, and the flesh of all freemen and bondmen, and of little and of great.

And I saw the beast, and the kings of the earth, and their armies gathered together to make war with him that sat upon the horse, and with his army.

XIX 11-19

Ah! Sun-flower

AH Sun-flower! weary of time,
  Who countest the steps of the Sun,
Seeking after that sweet golden clime
  Where the traveller's journey is done:

Where the Youth pined away with desire,
  And the pale Virgin shrouded in snow,
Arise from their graves and aspire
  Where my Sun-flower wishes to go.

WILLIAM BLAKE

To the Cuckoo

O BLITHE New-comer! I have heard,
　　I hear thee and rejoice.
O Cuckoo! shall I call thee Bird,
　　Or but a wandering Voice?

While I am lying on the grass
　　Thy twofold shout I hear;
From hill to hill it seems to pass
　　At once far off, and near.

Though babbling only to the Vale,
　　Of sunshine and of flowers,
Thou bringest unto me a tale
　　Of visionary hours.

Thrice welcome, darling of the Spring!
　　Even yet thou art to me
No bird, but an invisible thing,
　　A voice, a mystery;

The same whom in my schoolboy days
    I listened to; that Cry
Which made me look a thousand ways
    In bush, and tree, and sky.

To seek thee did I often rove
    Through woods and on the green;
And thou wert still a hope, a love;
    Still longed for, never seen.

And I can listen to thee yet;
    Can lie upon the plain
And listen, till I do beget
    That golden time again.

O blessed Bird! the earth we pace
    Again appears to be
An unsubstantial, faery place;
    That is fit home for Thee!

WILLIAM WORDSWORTH

On a Favourite Cat, Drowned in a Tub of Gold Fishes

Twas on a lofty vase's side,
Where China's gayest art had dyed
    The azure flowers that blow;
Demurest of the tabby kind,
The pensive Selima reclined,
    Gazed on the lake below.

Her conscious tail her joy declared;
The fair round face, the snowy beard.
    The velvet of her paws,
Her coat, that with the tortoise vies,
Her ears of jet, and emerald eyes,
    She saw; and purr'd applause.

Still had she gazed; but 'midst the tide
Two angel forms were seen to glide,
    The Genii of the stream:
Their scaly armour's Tyrian hue
Thro' richest purple to the view
    Betray'd a golden gleam.

The hapless Nymph with wonder saw:
A whisker first and then a claw,
    With many an ardent wish,
She stretch'd in vain to reach the prize.
What female heart can gold despise?
    What cat's averse to fish?

Presumptious Maid! with looks intent
Again she stretch'd, again she bent,
  Nor knew the gulf between.
(Malignant Fate sat by, and smiled.)
The slipp'ry verge her feet beguiled,
  She tumbled headlong in.

Eight times emerging from the flood
She mew'd to ev'ry wat'ry god,
  Some speedy aid to send.
No Dolphin came, no Nereid stirr'd:
Nor cruel Tom, nor Susan heard.
  A Fav'rite has no friend.

From hence, ye Beauties undeceived,
Know, one false step is ne'er retrieved,
  And be with caution bold.
Not all that tempts your wand'ring eyes
And heedles hearts, is lawful prize;
  Nor all that glisters, gold.

                              THOMAS GRAY

Elegy on the Death of
a Mad Dog

Good people all, of every sort,
　Give ear unto my song;
And if you find it wondrous short,—
　It cannot hold you long.

In Islington there was a man,
　Of whom the world might say,
That still a godly race he ran,—
　Whene'er he went to pray.

A kind and gentle heart he had,
　To comfort friends and foes;
The naked every day he clad,—
　When he put on his clothes.

And in that town a dog was found,
　As many dogs there be,
Both mongrel, puppy, whelp, and hound,
　And curs of low degree.

This dog and man at first were friends;
   But when a pique began,
The dog, to gain some private ends,
   Went mad, and bit the man.

Around from all the neighbouring streets
   The wondering neighbours ran,
And swore the dog had lost its wits,
   To bite so good a man.

The wound it seemed both sore and sad
   To every Christian eye;
And while they swore the dog was mad,
   They swore the man would die.

But soon a wonder came to light,
   That showed the rogues they lied;
The man recovered of the bite,
   The dog it was that died.

OLIVER GOLDSMITH

My Cats

I LIKE to toss him up and down
A heavy cat weighs half a Crown
With a hey do diddle my cat Brown.

I like to pinch him on the sly
When nobody is passing by
With a hey do diddle my cat Fry.

I like to ruffle up his pride
And watch him skip and turn aside
With a hey do diddle my cat Hyde.

Hey Brown and Fry and Hyde my cats
That sit on tombstone for your mats.

STEVIE SMITH

The Donkey

When fishes flew and forests walked
   And figs grew upon thorn,
Some moment when the moon was blood
   Then surely I was born.

With monstrous head and sickening cry
   And ears like errant wings,
The devil's walking parody
   On all four-footed things.

The tattered outlaw of the earth,
   Of ancient crooked will;
Starve, scourge, deride me: I am dumb,
   I keep my secret still.

Fools! For I also had my hour;
   One far fierce hour and sweet:
There was a shout about my ears,
   And palms before my feet.

G. K. CHESTERTON

The Eagle

He clasps the crag with crooked hands
Close to the sun in lonely lands,
Ringed with the azure world, he stands.

The wrinkled sea beneath him crawls;
He watches from his mountain walls,
And like a thunderbolt he falls.

ALFRED, LORD TENNYSON

Sonnet on the Sea

It keeps eternal whisperings around
Desolate shores, and with its mighty swell
Gluts twice ten thousand Caverns, till the spell
Of Hecate leaves them their old shadowy sound.
Often 'tis in such gentle temper found,
That scarcely will the very smallest shell
Be mov'd for days from where it sometime fell,
When last the winds of Heaven were unbound.
Oh ye! who have your eye-balls vex'd and tired,
Feast them upon the wideness of the Sea;
Oh ye! whose ears are dinn'd with uproar rude,
Or fed too much with cloying melody—
Sit ye near some old Cavern's Mouth, and brood
Until ye start, as if the sea-nymphs quir'd!

JOHN KEATS

The Peacock

What's riches to him
That has made a great peacock
With the pride of his eye?
The wind-beaten, stone-grey,
And desolate Three Rock
Would nourish his whim.
Live he or die
Amid wet rocks and heather,
His ghost will be gay
Adding feather to feather
For the pride of his eye.

W. B. YEATS

The Bird

Adventurous bird walking upon the air,
Like a schoolboy running and loitering, leaping and
    springing,
Pensively pausing, suddenly changing your mind
To turn at ease on the heel of a wing-tip. Where
In all the crystalline world was there to find
For your so delicate walking and airy winging
A floor so perfect, so firm and so fair,
And where a ceiling and walls so sweetly ringing,
Whenever you sing, to your clear singing?

The wide-winged soul itself can ask no more
Than such a pure, resilient and endless floor
For its strong-pinioned plunging and soaring and upward
    and upward springing.

EDWIN MUIR